Denzil and Abbie like music.

Abbie likes classical music.

Denzil likes hip hop and reggae music.

Denzil likes playing his guitar.

Abbie practices on her recorder.

Denzil is trying to sing as he plays the steel drum.

Abbie has lots of musical instruments.

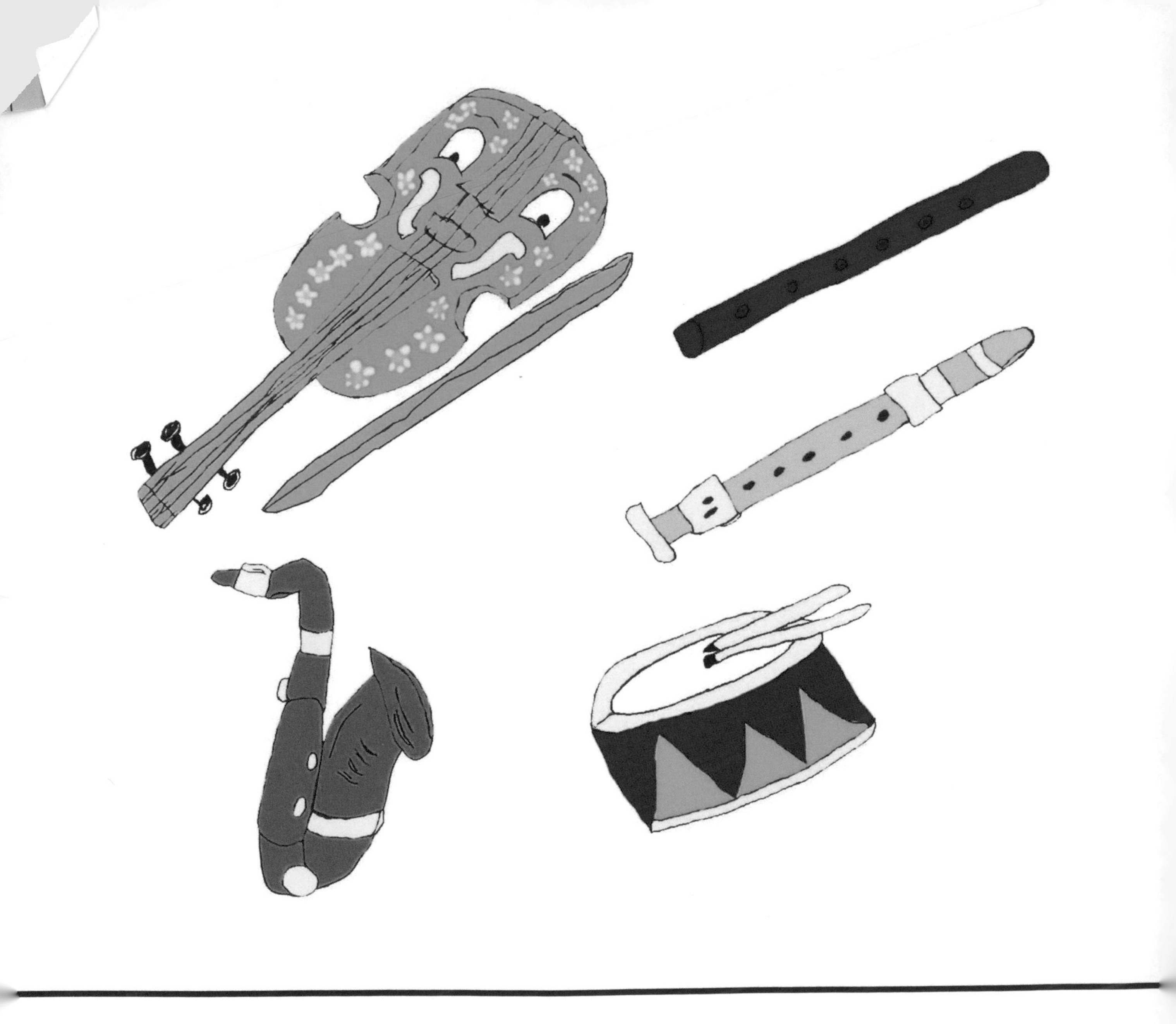

She has a violin, flute, recorder, saxophone and drum.

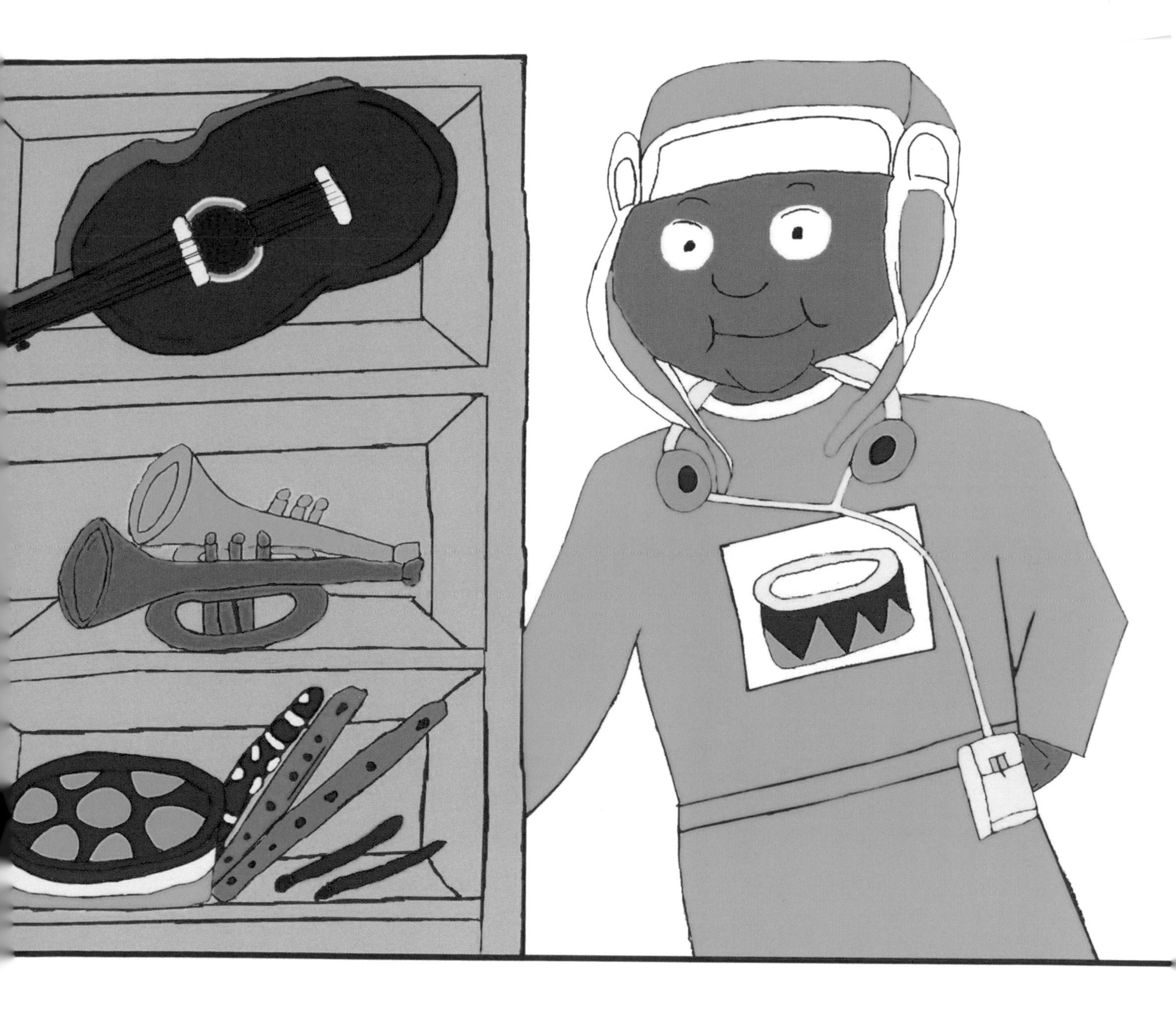

Denzil has lots of musical instruments too.

He has a guitar, trumpet, clarinet and a steel drum.

Denzil's friend calls round to play.

Abbie's friend calls round to play too.

Denzil's friend is called Ben.

Abbie's friend is called Belinda.

Abbie listens to her music box.

Belinda likes listening to the music box too.

Denzil is now playing music on his boombox.

Denzil and Ben are dancing to the music on the boombox.

Abbie and Belinda are also dancing to the music.

All the children are singing and dancing to the music.

Mum and Dad shout from the other room,

"Are you having a party in there? "

All the children shouted," Yes."

They have been dancing to the music for a long time.

The boombox has stopped and they are very tired.

"Time for some dinner now," said Mum.

The children, are all tired, and they have fallen a sleep.

"It's quiet in there," said Mum and Dad, "The party's over and they must be having a nap after all that dancing."

“Let them sleep,” said Mum. “ Yes, they are very good children,” said Dad.

CHILDREN BOOKS

BY DERRICK ALEXANDER

TITLE OF BOOKS

BARNABY AND CLARE

BEN AND BELINDA

DENZIL AND ABBIE

This book is dedicated to my daughter Sophie Alexander with lots of love from Dad.

DENZIL AND ABBIE

DENZIL AND ABBLE
Also available in ebook

DENZIL AND ABBIE

BEN AND BELINDA
B

BARNABY AND CLARE

83037905R00020

Made in the USA
Columbia, SC
22 December 2017